ABHIMANYU

ABHIMANYU, THE SON OF ARJUNA, THE PANDAVA AND SUBHADRA, KRISHNA'S SISTER, IS RENOWNED FOR THE VALOUR DISPLAYED BY HIM IN THE MAHABHARATA WAR.

HIS FATHER, ARJUNA COULD NOT HELP LOVING HIM MORE THAN HIS OTHER SONS.

ABHIMANYU SHALL GROW UP TO BE THE FOREMOST AMONG THE PANDAVAS AS WELL AS THE YADAVAS!

HUSH! ONE OUGHT NOT TO PRAISE ONE'S OWN CHILD THUS.

BUT ALAS! MISFORTUNE SOON BEFELL THE PANDAVAS WITH THEIR COUSINS, THE KAURAVAS, PLOTTING AGAINST THEM.

THE PANDAVAS ARE BECOMING TOO POWERFUL.

WE MUST TAKE THEIR KINGDOM AND GET RID OF THEM SOMEHOW!

I HAVE IT! YUDHISHTHIRA HAS A WEAKNESS FOR GAMBLING. LET US INVITE HIM TO A GAME AND MAKE THE DICE OBEY US.

THE KAURAVAS CARRIED OUT THEIR WICKED PLOT.

YUDHISHTHIRA, YOU'VE LOST AGAIN.

YOU HAD PLEDGED YOUR KINGDOM. NOW GIVE IT UP. GO INTO EXILE WITH YOUR BROTHERS INTO THE FORESTS FOR THIRTEEN YEARS.

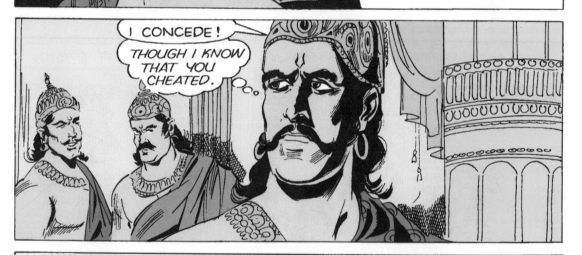

I CONCEDE!

THOUGH I KNOW THAT YOU CHEATED.

THE PANDAVAS SET OUT FOR THE FORESTS WITH THE SORROWFUL CITIZENS WHO HAD GATHERED TO BID THEM FAREWELL, IN ATTENDANCE.

ABHIMANYU WAS A MERE CHILD WHEN THESE EVENTS TOOK PLACE. BUT HE WAS WELL LOOKED AFTER BY HIS MOTHER.

YOUR VALOUR SHALL ONE DAY AVENGE THIS HUMILIATION.

HE GREW UP TO BE A VALIANT YOUTH AND KRISHNA'S FAVOURITE NEPHEW.

I SHALL FIGHT THE KAURAVAS AND WIN BACK OUR KINGDOM.

WELL SPOKEN, ABHIMANYU, WELL SPOKEN!

HE WAS LOVED AND ADMIRED BY ALL WHO KNEW HIM.

ABHIMANYU HAS INHERITED THE QUALITIES OF KRISHNA AND THE PANDAVAS.

YES. HE HAS YUDHISHTHIRA'S PATIENCE, KRISHNA'S CONDUCT, BHIMA'S STRENGTH, THE GENTLENESS OF NAKULA AND SAHADEVA AND ARJUNA'S LOOKS, PROWESS AND SCRIPTURAL KNOWLEDGE.

MEANWHILE THIRTEEN YEARS HAD PASSED. THE PANDAVAS WERE AT THE COURT OF KING VIRATA, IN DISGUISE AND IN THE LAST YEAR OF THEIR EXILE.

WHILE THERE, ARJUNA HELPED VIRATA'S SON UTTARA TO TRIUMPH OVER A KAURAVA ATTACK.

AFTER ARJUNA AND UTTARA RETURNED FROM THE BATTLE, THE PANDAVAS DISCLOSED THEIR IDENTITY TO VIRATA.

BHIMA.

I AM ARJUNA.

I AM YUDHISHTHIRA.

NAKULA.

SAHADEVA.

ARJUNA, I OFFER YOU MY DAUGHTER UTTARĀ.

O KING, I ACCEPT YOUR DAUGHTER AS MY DAUGHTER-IN-LAW.

WHY NOT AS YOUR WIFE?

I CANNOT. I WAS HER TEACHER ONCE IN MUSIC AND DANCE.

MY SON, THE VALIANT AND GODLIKE ABHIMANYU, IS KRISHNA'S FAVOURITE NEPHEW. HE SURPASSES ALL IN LOOKS AND IN THE KNOWLEDGE OF WEAPONS. HE IS FIT TO BE YOUR SON-IN-LAW AND UTTARA'S HUSBAND.

VIRATA WAS AGREEABLE.

WITH YOU AS THE FATHER OF MY SON-IN-LAW, I HAVE NOTHING ELSE TO ASK FOR.

YUDHISHTHIRA, TOO, GAVE HIS ASSENT AND WORD WAS SENT TO KRISHNA TO BRING SUBHADRA AND ABHIMANYU AND THEIR KINSMEN TO VIRATA'S KINGDOM.

THE WEDDING OF ABHIMANYU AND UTTARA WAS SOLEMNISED AMIDST GREAT FEASTING AND REJOICING. IT WAS ATTENDED BY A HOST OF FRIENDLY KINGS OF NEIGHBOURING KINGDOMS.

AFTER THE WEDDING THE PANDAVAS HELD A COUNCIL.

I WOULD LIKE TO WIN BACK OUR KINGDOM WITHOUT BLOODSHED.

LET ME GO TO HASTINAPURA AND SEE WHAT I CAN DO.

BUT KING DURYODHANA, THE KAURAVA, WAS OBSTINATE.

I REFUSE THEM EVEN AN INCH OF LAND. LET THEM FIGHT AND TAKE IT IF THEY CAN.

KRISHNA'S MISS ON FAILED.

AND IT WAS WAR BETWEEN THE PANDAVAS AND THE KAURAVAS - THE TERRIBLE WAR OF THE MAHABHARATA - IN WHICH PRACTICALLY ALL THE KINGS OF THOSE TIMES FOUGHT, AS ALLIES, ON ONE SIDE OR THE OTHER.

IT IS NOT YET NOON AND OUR ARMY IS BEING ROUTED BY THE KAURAVAS.

BHEESHMA, THE GRANDSIRE IS CREATING HAVOC WHEREVER HE GOES.

ABHIMANYU WHEN HE HEARD THIS CHARGED UPON BHEESHMA.

A MERE STRIPLING OF A BOY BUT WHAT A FINE WARRIOR! HE SEEMS TO BE EVERYWHERE.

THUS ABHIMANYU DISTINGUISHED HIMSELF ON THE VERY FIRST DAY OF THE BATTLE.

SOON OTHER WARRIORS CAME TO RELIEVE HIM AND BHEESHMA TURNED HIS ATTENTION TO THEM. BUT THE FIRST DAY WAS A BAD ONE FOR THE PANDAVAS. THAT NIGHT—

BHEESHMA HAS DECIMATED OUR ARMIES ON THIS VERY FIRST DAY OF BATTLE.

WHY DO YOU WORRY? YOU HAVE VALIANT BROTHERS, NEPHEWS AND ALLIES. MOREOVER SHIKHANDI IS DESTINED TO BE THE CAUSE OF BHEESHMA'S DEATH.

THUS KRISHNA CONSOLED AND ENCOURAGED THE PANDAVAS.

ON THE SECOND DAY, THE KAURAVAS INTOXICATED BY THEIR EARLY VICTORY, WERE OVER CONFIDENT AND CARELESS. TILL—

IT IS WISE TO END THE FIGHT FOR THE DAY AND RETIRE. WE HAVE SUFFERED HEAVY REVERSES AND OUR TROOPS ARE WEARY.

AND THE PANDAVAS WON THE DAY.

SO THE BATTLE WENT ON, SOMETIMES FAVOURING THE PANDAVAS, SOMETIMES THE KAURAVAS.

TILL AT LAST ON THE TENTH DAY BHEESHMA FELL, AT THE HANDS OF ARJUNA SHIELDED BY SHIKHANDI.

DRONA WAS MADE COMMANDER OF THE KAURAVA ARMIES.

WITH YOU AS OUR LEADER WE CAN EASILY DEFEAT YUDHISHTHIRA AND HIS MIGHTY ALLIES.

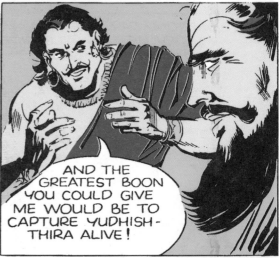

AND THE GREATEST BOON YOU COULD GIVE ME WOULD BE TO CAPTURE YUDHISHTHIRA ALIVE!

DRONA TRIED BUT FAILED. THAT EVENING THE KAURAVAS HELD A SPECIAL CONFERENCE.

WE CAN NEVER TAKE YUDHISHTHIRA AS LONG AS ARJUNA IS BY HIS SIDE.

IF ARJUNA CAN BE DRAWN AWAY I CAN BREAK THE PANDAVA TROOP FORMATION AND CAPTURE YUDHISHTHIRA.

THAT CAN BE DONE. LEAVE IT TO US.

THE PLOY WAS SUCCESSFUL. ARJUNA WAS DRAWN AWAY, AND DRONA ATTACKED. THE ATTACK WAS SO FIERCE THAT THE PANDAVAS WITH ARJUNA AWAY, WERE LOSING GROUND.

AT LAST YUDHISHTHIRA APPROACHED ABHIMANYU, PLACING THE BURDEN ON HIS YOUNG SHOULDERS.

ONLY YOU, ARJUNA, KRISHNA AND PRADYUMNA KNOW HOW TO BREAK THROUGH DRONA'S CIRCULAR FORMATION OF TROOPS. NONE OF THEM IS HERE, BUT YOU.

SON, WILL YOU LEAD US?

I WILL GLADLY TRY TO BREAK THROUGH THE FORMATION BUT......

...I DO NOT KNOW HOW TO COME OUT OF IT, IF I AM OVERPOWERED AND IN DANGER.

BREAK THE FORMATION AND MAKE WAY FOR US TO ENTER. WE WILL FOLLOW CLOSE UPON YOUR HEELS AND PROTECT YOU.

I WILL BREAK THROUGH IT AND SLAUGHTER THE KAURAVAS. MY ACHIEVEMENT TODAY SHALL EMBELLISH THE FAIR NAME OF THE PANDAVAS AND THE YADAVAS.

MAY YOUR MIGHT INCREASE EVEN AS YOU SPEAK.

ABHIMANYU COMMANDED HIS CHARIOTEER.

PROCEED! PROCEED! URGE THE HORSES TOWARDS DRONA'S TROOPS.

THE PANDAVAS HAVE PLACED A HEAVY BURDEN ON YOU TODAY. THINK WELL BEFORE YOU PROCEED.

DRONA IS AN ADEPT IN THE ART OF WARFARE. YOU HAVE BEEN BROUGHT UP IN COMFORT AND ARE NOT USED TO THE STRAIN OF WAR.

I AM ARJUNA'S SON AND KRISHNA'S NEPHEW. DRIVE ON.

THEY REACHED DRONA'S ARRAY WITH THE PANDAVAS AND THEIR ALLIES FOLLOWING CLOSE BEHIND.

LOOK! HERE HE COMES! ABHIMANYU!

THEN LIKE A PROUD YOUNG LION FALLING UPON A HERD OF ELEPHANTS, ABHIMANYU RUSHED AT DRONA.

THE HEROES FOUGHT ON AND THE TROOPS SLAUGHTERED ONE ANOTHER.

WHILE THE TERRIFYING BATTLE RAGED, ABHIMANYU, BREAKING THE CIRCULAR ARRAY, ENTERED IT UNDER THE VERY NOSE OF DRONA.

HE IS INDEED THE GREATEST AMONG ARCHERS! HE IS CAPABLE OF DESTROYING AN ENTIRE ARMY IF HE CHOOSES!

BUT ALAS FOR HIM, BEFORE THE PANDAVAS AND THEIR WARRIORS COULD FOLLOW HIM, THE BREACH WAS EFFICIENTLY AND EFFECTIVELY CLOSED BY JAYADRATHA.

AND ABHIMANYU WAS ALONE.

BUT HE FOUGHT BRAVELY AND FELLED THE KAURAVA WARRIORS, COVERING THE EARTH WITH THEIR MUTILATED BODIES.

THE KAURAVA TROOPS TERRIFIED BY THIS ONSLAUGHT, TRIED TO FLEE ON CHARIOTS AND ELEPHANTS FORSAKING THEIR WOUNDED KINSMEN AND FRIENDS.

WE WILL NEVER CONQUER THIS MIGHTY HERO.

LET US ESCAPE WHILE THERE IS STILL LIFE LEFT WITHIN US.

WHEN DURYODHANA SAW HIS ARMY BEING THUS ROUTED BY ABHIMAN-YU, HE WAS FURIOUS AND RUSHED TOWARDS HIM.

DRONA WAS ALARMED.

SAVE THE KING! ABHIMANYU KILLS ALL MEN HE AIMS AT. AND NOW HIS AIM IS ON THE KING OF THE KAURAVAS.

A GREAT NUMBER OF WARRIORS IMMEDIATELY WENT TO DURYODHANA'S RESCUE.

AND SUCCEEDED IN DRAWING HIM AWAY.

BUT ABHIMANYU WAS ENRAGED WHEN HE FOUND HIS PRIZE TARGET BEING SNATCHED AWAY.

HE VENTED HIS ANGER ON THE WARRIORS WHO HAD PROTECTED DURYODHANA.

FORGETTING THE CODE OF WAR CONDUCT, A NUMBER OF WARRIORS, LED BY DRONA, JOINTLY ATTACKED YOUNG ABHIMANYU.

NOW HE CAN'T ESCAPE DEATH AT OUR HANDS.

IT SEEMED IMPOSSIBLE TO CONTROL THEIR ADVANCES. BUT A SHOWER OF ARROWS FROM ABHIMANYU'S BOW HELD THEM.

ONE OF THE WARRIORS, ASMAKA, RUSHED HIS CHARIOT AT GREAT SPEED TOWARDS ABHIMANYU.

ABHIMANYU'S ARROW KILLED HIM.

KARNA THEN MADE A DASH TOWARDS ABHIMANYU.

BUT HIS ARMOUR WAS PIERCED.

ABHIMANYU THEN WOUNDED SHALYA SO BADLY THAT THE GREAT WARRIOR COULD NOT EVEN MOVE FROM HIS SEAT.

SHALYA'S BROTHER RUSHED FORWARD.

I MUST AVENGE THE DEFEAT OF MY BROTHER.

ONE SINGLE ARROW FROM ABHIMANYU'S BOW...

...BROKE HIS CHARIOT TO PIECES.

21

SO GREAT WAS THE SKILL DISPLAYED BY ABHIMANYU THAT EVEN DRONA WHO LED THE ATTACK, ADMIRED HIM.

HE STANDS UNEQUALLED AS A BOWMAN. IF HE WISHES HE CAN WIPE OUT THIS WHOLE HOST, SINGLE-HANDED.

DURYODHANA, WHO OVERHEARD THIS REMARK, BECAME VERY ANGRY.

DUHSHASANA! LISTEN! HOW PARTIAL DRONACHARYA IS TOWARDS ARJUNA'S SON. WE MUST KILL THE BOY SOON.

I'LL KILL HIM. THIS VERY INSTANT.

THE CHARIOTS OF ABHIMANYU AND DUHSHASANA MADE WONDERFUL MOVEMENTS AGAINST EACH OTHER.

VERY SOON, DUHSHASANA FELL SENSELESS IN HIS CHARIOT, STRUCK BY ONE OF ABHIMANYU'S ARROWS.

DUHSHASANA'S CHARIOTEER RUSHED AWAY FROM THE BATTLE SCENE TO SAVE HIS MASTER.

IT WAS NOW KARNA'S TURN. HE SENT A SHOWER OF ARROWS.

ABHIMANYU INTERCEPTED THEM ALL.

AND SENT A FRESH SHOWER OF ARROWS IN THE DIRECTION OF KARNA.

KARNA HAD TO RETREAT.

DURYODHANA'S SON, LAKSHMANA, A BRAVE WARRIOR, RUSHED TOWARDS ABHIMANYU IN A BID TO SAVE THE HONOUR OF THE KAURAVA ARMY.

KARNA, DRONA AND MANY OTHER RETREATING WARRIORS, NOW CAME BACK TO SUPPORT LAKSHMANA IN HIS FIGHT.

BUT A SHARP ARROW FROM ABHIMAN-YU'S BOW CAME WHIZZING...

...AND PIERCED LAKSHMANA.

SEEING THE DEAD BODY OF HIS YOUNG SON, DURYODHANA WAS FURIOUS.

KILL! KILL THE WICKED ABHIMANYU!

AT THIS COMMAND OF DURYODHANA, DRONA, KARNA AND THE OTHER WARRIORS IN THE KAURAVA ARMY MOUNTED A FRESH ATTACK ON ABHIMANYU.

KARNA TURNED TO DRONA.

TELL US HOW TO KILL HIM BEFORE HE SLAYS US ALL.

YOU WILL NEVER BE ABLE TO PIERCE HIS ARMOUR.

AIM AT THE REINS OF HIS HORSES AND CUT THEM OFF. HE WILL BE DISABLED. THEN ATTACK FROM BEHIND.

KARNA CUT OFF THE REINS OF HIS HORSES.

FROM BEHIND, HE SHOT AN ARROW THAT BROKE ABHIMANYU'S BOW.

SOON ABHIMANYU'S HORSES LAY DEAD AND HIS CHARIOTEER WAS KILLED.

NOW HE JUMPED TO THE GROUND AND...

...WHIRLED HIS SWORD AND SHIELD. ALONE IN THE FIELD, HE HELD HIS GROUND AGAINST MANY WARRIORS.

SOON AN ARROW FROM DRONA BROKE HIS SWORD...

...AND AN ARROW FROM KARNA HIS SHIELD.

THUS ABHIMANYU WAS TOTALLY DISABLED. BUT UNDAUNTED, HE PICKED UP THE WHEEL OF HIS CHARIOT...

...AND BEGAN WHIRLING IT AGAINST HIS UNFAIR AND UNJUST ENEMIES. BUT HE WAS COMPLETELY ENCIRCLED.

ARROWS FROM MANY BOWS CAME WHIZZING FROM ALL DIRECTIONS.

AND SOON THE WHEEL LAY BROKEN TO PIECES.

ABHIMANYU THEN PICKED UP A MACE THAT WAS LYING ON THE FIELD.

DUHSHASANA'S SON CLOSED IN.

WHILE FIGHTING
BOTH FELL TO THE GROUND.

BUT DUHSHASANA'S SON WAS
THE FIRST TO GET UP.

AND BEFORE ABHIMANYU COULD RISE, HE BROUGHT THE MACE DOWN ON HIS SKULL.

WHEN THE MIGHTY HERO FELL, LIKE SAVAGES THE KAURAVA WARRIORS DANCED AROUND HIS DEAD BODY.

NOT ONE OF THEM, HOWEVER, OUTLIVED THE WAR. ARJUNA, BHEEMA AND THE MIGHTY PANDAVAS AVENGED ABHIMANYU BY KILLING THEM ALL IN THE BATTLES THAT FOLLOWED AT KURUKSHETRA...

...AND ABHIMANYU'S BRAVERY IS REMEMBERED TILL THIS DAY.

GHATOTKACHA

THE CHIVALROUS DEMON

The route to your roots

GHATOTKACHA

He may have looked like a demon, but Ghatatkacha was a guardian angel - always ready to help, always cheerful. The Pandava brother, Bheema, was lucky to have him as a son, for he saved his life more than once. And if it were not for this brave young rakshasa, the Kauravas may well have been the victors of the famous battle of Mahabharata.

Script
Lakshmi Seshadri

Illustrations
Umesh Burande

Editor
Anant Pai

Cover illustration by: Khalap

GHATOTKACHA

THE KAURAVA PRINCES AND THE ORPHANED PANDAVA PRINCES WERE COUSINS. THEY GREW UP TOGETHER AT HASTINAPURA IN THE CHARGE OF THEIR GRAND-UNCLE, BHEESHMA.

BUT THE KAURAVAS WERE JEALOUS OF THEIR COUSINS.

UNCLE BHEESHMA IS PARTIAL TO THE PANDAVAS.

THE PEOPLE TOO LOVE THEM MORE THAN US.

JEALOUSY SOON TURNED INTO HATRED. DURYODHANA, THE ELDEST KAURAVA THOUGHT OF A WICKED PLAN.

WE WILL SEND THEM TO VARANAVATA TO LIVE IN THE HOUSE OF LAC. AND THEN SET FIRE TO IT.

WHEN THE PANDAVAS ARRIVED AT VARANAVATA, YUDHISHTHIRA, THE ELDEST OF THEM TURNED TO THE OTHERS—

THIS IS A TRAP!

THE PANDAVAS SECRETLY HAD A TUNNEL MADE FOR ESCAPE.

BEFORE WE LEAVE, WE MUST SET FIRE TO THIS HOUSE.

AFTER SETTING THE HOUSE ON FIRE, THE PANDAVAS AND THEIR MOTHER, KUNTI, ESCAPED THROUGH THE TUNNEL.

WHEN THEY WERE DEEP IN THE FOREST—

I AM TIRED, MOTHER.

I KNOW. BUT WE CANNOT STOP NOW. BHEEMA, CAN YOU CARRY HIM?

BHEEMA WAS THE STRONGEST OF THEM ALL.

I CAN CARRY ALL OF YOU.

WHEN THEY HAD TRAVELLED FAR ENOUGH—

NOW WE MAY REST.

YOU ARE ALL TIRED. I AM NOT. YOU SLEEP. I'LL KEEP WATCH.

HIDIMBA, A RAKSHASA WAS THE MASTER OF THAT FOREST.

SISTER HIDIMBAA! I SMELL HUMANS. BRING THEM HERE. WE SHALL FEAST ON FRESH MEAT.

M..M...M...M..! MY MOUTH WATERS!

WHEN HIDIMBAA CAME IN SEARCH OF THE PANDAVAS SHE SAW BHEEMA FIRST.

HOW HANDSOME HE IS! I DON'T WANT TO EAT HIM. I'LL MARRY HIM.

I SHALL CHANGE MYSELF INTO A BEAUTIFUL GIRL. THEN HE WILL FALL IN LOVE WITH ME.

MEANWHILE—

HIDIMBAA IS LATE. HAS SHE...? IS SHE...? NO IT CANNOT BE! YET I WONDER...

AS I SUSPECTED! SHE HAS CHANGED HER FORM AND IS MAKING EYES AT THAT HUMAN.

HIDIMBA CHALLENGED BHEEMA AND THEY FOUGHT.

THE NOISE AWOKE KUNTI.

YUDHISHTHIRA! GET UP!

KUNTI, HIDIMBAA AND YUDHISHTHIRA RUSHED FORWARD.

BHEEMA! BE CAREFUL!

DO NOT FEAR MOTHER, YOUR BRAVE SON WILL WIN.

MY BLESSINGS, BHEEMA!

HIDIMBA WAS KILLED. KUNTI NOW TURNED TO HIDIMBAA.

YOU ARE VERY BEAUTIFUL! WHO ARE YOU?

THAT WAS MY BROTHER. I LOVE YOUR SON. I DESERTED MY BROTHER FOR HIM.

I HAVE NO ONE NOW. LET ME MARRY YOUR SON, MOTHER.

WE ARE HOMELESS.

I AM THE MISTRESS OF THIS FOREST. STAY HERE AS LONG AS YOU WISH.

KUNTI CONSULTED YUDHISHTHIRA.

LET HER MARRY BHEEMA.

IT IS ONLY FAIR, MOTHER.

SO BHEEMA MARRIED HIDIMBAA.

HIDIMBAA WAS A DEVOTED DAUGHTER-IN-LAW.

MOTHER, I MAY LIVE WITH YOU TILL YOUR GRANDSON IS BORN. THEN WE WILL HAVE TO PART.

NOT LONG AFTER, BHEEMA'S SON, GHATOTKACHA, WAS BORN. BEING A RAKSHASA HE KNEW ALL THEIR MAGIC AND WAS FULL-GROWN AT BIRTH.

FATHER! I AM THE LORD OF THIS FOREST. WHEN-EVER YOU THINK OF ME I WILL COME AND SERVE YOU.

WE WILL GO ON! GOD BLESS YOU.

THE PANDAVAS WENT THEIR WAY AND GHATOTKACHA LIVED WITH HIS MOTHER IN THEIR FOREST.

MANY YEARS PASSED BY. THE PANDAVAS BECAME THE RULERS OF INDRAPRASTHA WHERE THEY BUILT A BEAUTIFUL PALACE. YUDHISHTHIRA PERFORMED THE RAJASUYA SACRIFICE. THE KAURAVAS WERE JEALOUS OF THEIR SUCCESS.

WE MUST DO SOMETHING. THE PANDAVAS ARE TOO POPULAR AND PROSPEROUS.

I HAVE AN IDEA. LET US INVITE YUDHISHTHIRA TO PLAY DICE.

WE WILL MARK THE DICE AND CHEAT HIM.

SO THE KAURAVAS INVITED THE PANDAVAS TO HASTINAPURA.

SHALL WE BEGIN?

A KING CANNOT REFUSE. WE WILL PLAY.

YUDHISHTHIRA PLAYED AND LOST ALL HIS WEALTH.

COME! STAKE YOUR KINGDOM NOW.

AGREED!

HE LOST HIS KINGDOM TOO. BUT HE CONTINUED TO PLAY.

WILL YOU AGREE TO GO TO THE FOREST FOR 13 YEARS IF YOU LOSE? IF YOU WIN I'LL GIVE BACK YOUR KINGDOM.

ALL RIGHT!

YUDHISHTHIRA LOST. THE PANDAVAS HAD TO LEAVE FOR THE FOREST, WITH DRAUPADI, THEIR QUEEN.

WHEN THEY HAD GONE, ARJUNA'S WIFE, SUBHADRA, A YADAVA PRINCESS, TOOK THEIR SON, ABHIMANYU, TO THE YADAVA KINGDOM.

ABHIMANYU, YOUR UNCLE BALARAMA HAS GONE BACK ON HIS WORD. HE IS GIVING VATSALA TO *LAKSHMANA.

MY REPUTATION IS AT STAKE. LET US GO TO DWARAKA.

ON THE WAY TO DWARAKA—

DRIVE QUICKLY, ABHIMANYU. I DON'T FEEL SAFE.

SUDDENLY—

HOW DARE YOU TRESPASS. I SHALL KILL YOU!

BUT ABHIMANYU WAS UNDAUNTED.

I'LL KILL YOU FIRST!

* DURYODHANA'S SON.

●BALARAMA'S DAUGHTER

AFTER A TOUGH FIGHT—

ALAS! HOW DID A MERE HUMAN OVERPOWER YOU?

WHO IS HE?

THE SON OF BHEEMA, THE PANDAVA.

I AM ARJUNA'S WIFE, SUBHADRA... MY SON...

STOP! ABHIMANYU! HE IS YOUR UNCLE BHEEMA'S SON! YOUR COUSIN!

BROTHER! FORGIVE ME! I DID NOT KNOW YOU.

SUBHADRA TOLD HER STORY.

SISTER! MY BROTHER, BALARAMA, HAS GONE BACK ON HIS WORD.

ABHIMANYU WAS BETROTHED TO HIS DAUGHTER, VATSALA.

BUT NOW THAT ARJUNA IS IN EXILE, VATSALA IS TO MARRY LAKSHMANA, THE SON OF THE KAURAVA, DURYODHANA.

WE ARE GOING TO DWARAKA TO TRY AND PREVENT IT.

GHATOTKACHA PROMISED TO HELP THEM.

DON'T WORRY, MOTHER! TAKE OUR GUESTS HOME. I WILL SETTLE THIS MATTER.

GHATOTKACHA CALLED HIS RAKSHASAS.

MEN! GO TO DWARAKA. BUY UP ALL THE SHOPS THERE AND...

WHEN HE HAD FINISHED—

THEN WAIT FOR MY SIGNAL.

THE RAKSHASAS WENT TO DWARAKA AND BOUGHT UP ALL THE SHOPS. THEN—

NEW CLOTHES FOR OLD.

DO YOU REALLY EXCHANGE THEM?

UNBELIEVABLE! SHOPS IN DWARAKA EXCHANGE OLD CLOTHES FOR NEW ONES.

THE KAURAVAS WHO HAD COME FOR THE WEDDING, FLOCKED TO THE SHOPS.

THESE NEW CLOTHES ARE OF A SUPERIOR QUALITY.

WHAT A NOVEL WAY OF ENTERTAINING THE BRIDEGROOM'S PARTY.

MEANWHILE GHATOTKACHA ENTERED VATSALA'S ROOM.

I COME FROM ABHIMANYU! READ THIS.

VATSALA READ ABHIMANYU'S MESSAGE.

COME! SIT DOWN AND DO NOT BE AFRAID.

MY LORD TELLS ME TO OBEY YOU.

GHATOTKACHA PICKED UP VATSALA'S BED AND FLEW OUT OF THE WINDOW.

YOU SHALL SOON BE WITH ABHIMANYU AND MOTHER SUBHADRA.

GHATOTKACHA LEFT VATSALA WITH ABHIMANYU AND RETURNED TO DWARAKA.

I MUST NOW TRANSFORM MYSELF TO LOOK LIKE VATSALA...

...AND TAKE HER PLACE.

THE NEXT MORNING THE BRIDE WAS LED TO THE MARRIAGE HALL.

I SHALL NOW SQUEEZE HIS HAND TILL IT BREAKS.

O..O..O! HOW TIGHT HER GRIP IS!

THE NEXT DAY, SUBHADRA ARRIVED AT DWARAKA WITH ABHIMANYU AND HIS BRIDE.

BROTHER! BLESS THEM! THEY WERE MARRIED YESTERDAY, THANKS TO GHATOTKACHA.

FATHER! FORGIVE ME! I LOVE ABHIMANYU.

I AM SORRY SISTER! I SHOULD HAVE KNOWN BETTER.

ABHIMANYU LIVED HAPPILY AT DWARAKA WITH VATSALA AND SUBHADRA.

WHEN THEIR EXILE WAS OVER, THE PANDAVAS RETURNED FROM THE FOREST. THE KAURAVAS WOULD NOT GIVE BACK THEIR KINGDOM. SO THE PANDAVAS COLLECTED THEIR ARMIES TO FIGHT THEM. LORD KRISHNA WAS ON THE SIDE OF THE PANDAVAS—

BHEEMA! YOU MUST CALL GHATOTKACHA. WE WILL NEED HIS HELP. DON'T YOU AGREE, KRISHNA?

YES. HE HELPED MY SISTER SUBHADRA WHEN SHE NEEDED HIM.

NOW HE WILL BE ONLY TOO GLAD TO HELP US.

I HAVE BUT TO THINK OF HIM.

GHATOTKACHA APPEARED WITH HIS RAKSHASA FORCES.

FATHER! HERE I AM!

THE MAHABHARATA WAR BEGAN. ON THE FOURTH DAY OF THE WAR, KING BHAGADATTA ATTACKED BHEEMA.

I WISH GHATOTKACHA WERE HERE TO HELP ME.

GHATOTKACHA AT ONCE CAME TO BHEEMA'S HELP.

THEY KILLED SO MANY KAURAVAS THAT DURYODHANA SOUNDED THE RETREAT.

WE HAVE DONE WELL TODAY, GHATOTKACHA.

THE NEXT DAY, BHAGADATTA RETALIATED BY ATTACKING THE PANDAVAS AND KILLING MANY OF THEM.

GHATOTKACHA CAME THERE. THE KAURAVAS SAW MANY OF THEIR FRIENDS LYING DEAD.

HOW DID SO MANY OF THEM DIE ALL OF A SUDDEN?

WH...WHAT... HOW? LET US SAVE OUR LIVES!

NOT REALISING THAT IT WAS MERELY AN ILLUSION, THEY RAN AWAY FROM THE BATTLEFIELD.

HA! HA! HOW EASILY THEY WERE TRICKED.

ON THE THIRTEENTH DAY OF THE WAR, ABHIMANYU WAS KILLED.

JAYADRATHA WAS THE CAUSE OF ABHIMANYU'S DEATH. ARJUNA SWORE TO KILL HIM BY SUNSET NEXT DAY.

IF I DON'T SUCCEED, I WILL KILL MYSELF!

DURYODHANA CALLED HIS GENERALS TO HIM.

WE MUST GUARD JAYADRATHA FROM ARJUNA.

IF HE IS ALIVE AT SUNSET, ARJUNA WILL KILL HIMSELF AND THE WAR WILL END.

BEFORE SUNSET THE NEXT DAY, ARJUNA, WITH LORD KRISHNA'S HELP, KILLED JAYADRATHA.

DURYODHANA TAUNTED HIS GENERALS, DRONA AND KARNA.

YOU HAVE NOT FOUGHT WELL. THAT IS WHY JAYADRATHA WAS KILLED.

DON'T BLAME US. WE DID OUR BEST.

WE WILL GO BACK AND CONTINUE THE BATTLE TILL JAYADRATHA IS AVENGED.

DRONA AND KARNA FOUGHT SO WELL THAT THE PANDAVAS WERE HARD-PRESSED. YUDHISHTHIRA CALLED ARJUNA AND KRISHNA.

MY ARMIES SUFFER! GO AND FIGHT KARNA.

IT IS NOT YET TIME FOR ARJUNA TO MEET KARNA!

LORD KRISHNA SENT FOR GHATOTKACHA. WHEN HE CAME —

DEAR GHATOTKACHA! HELP OUR ARMIES AGAINST KARNA.

I WILL FINISH HIM.

RAKSHASA-POWER INCREASES BY NIGHT.

I SHALL EASILY DEFEAT KARNA WITH MY MAGIC.

21

*DISC.

KARNA DESTROYED IT WITH ARROWS, SMILING ALL THE TIME.

GHATOTKACHA CREATED A MOUNTAIN BY HIS MAGIC. FROM THE MOUNTAIN CAME STREAMS OF WEAPONS.

KARNA DESTROYED THE MOUNTAIN WITH THE VAJRA ASTRA.*

* THE VAJRA ASTRA IS HARD LIKE A THUNDERBOLT AND CAN BREAK EVEN MOUNTAINS.

GHATOTKACHA MADE A DARK CLOUD WHICH RAINED DOWN STONES.

KARNA BLEW IT AWAY WITH A VAYU ASTRA.*

*VAYU ASTRA PRODUCES A STRONG WIND AS IT IS GUIDED BY THE GOD OF WIND.

GHATOTKACHA SENT TREES FLYING AT HIM.

KARNA DESTROYED THEM WITH ARROWS.

GHATOTKACHA FELL DOWN AS IF DEAD.

THE PANDAVA SOLDIERS GRIEVED.

ALAS! HE IS DEAD!

SUDDENLY THERE WERE GHATOTKACHAS EVERYWHERE.

KARNA SHOT ARROWS AT THEM ALL.

GHATOTKACHA OPENED HIS MOUTH WIDE AND SWALLOWED THE ARROWS.

KARNA ONLY SENT MORE.

GHATOTKACHA BECAME TINY AND ELUDED THEM.

THEN HE BECAME INVISIBLE AND SENT SHOWERS OF FIERY WEAPONS.

THE TERRIFIED KAURAVA FORCES APPEALED TO KARNA.

SAVE US, KARNA!

YOUR ARROWS ARE NOT POWERFUL ENOUGH.

YOU ARE OUR PROTECTOR.

USE YOUR SHAKTI!

THE SHAKTI HAD BEEN GIVEN TO KARNA BY INDRA, KING OF THE GODS.

IT IS MY WEAPON. IT WILL KILL ANYONE. BUT YOU CAN USE IT ONLY ONCE. IT WILL RETURN TO ME AFTER THAT.

KARNA HESITATED TO USE THE SHAKTI.

I RESERVED IT FOR ARJUNA! I MUST NOT WASTE IT.

BUT THE CRIES OF THE WARRIORS WERE PITIABLE.

WE CAN'T SEE THE ENEMY.

WE HAVE NO SAVIOUR!

YET THE WEAPONS HIT US.

I CAN'T LET OUR WARRIORS SUFFER.

I WILL HAVE TO USE THE SHAKTI.

KARNA PICKED UP THE SHAKTI AND THREW IT.

IT ENTERED GHATOTKACHA'S HEART AND WENT UP TO HEAVEN AS A FLASH OF LIGHT.

GHATOTKACHA KNEW HE WAS DYING. HE MADE HIS BODY ENORMOUS, JUMPED INTO THE AIR...

...AND FELL, CRUSHING A WHOLE KAURAVA REGIMENT UNDER HIM.

YUDHISHTHIRA TOOK GHATOTKACHA'S HEAD ON HIS LAP AND WEPT, WHILE KRISHNA LOOKED ON, SMILING.

ALAS! GHATOTKACHA, MY BRAVE CHILD! HOW CAN YOU SMILE, KRISHNA?

GHATOTKACHA HAS SAVED ARJUNA. KARNA'S SHAKTI IS SPENT. NOW HE IS POWERLESS TO KILL ARJUNA.

BHEEMA CAME TO MOURN HIS SON.

EVEN IN HIS DEATH GHATOTKACHA HAS HELPED US.

HE DIED IN A GOOD CAUSE. HIS DEATH WILL BE JUSTIFIED BY THE PANDAVA VICTORY.

AMAR CHITRA KATHA

5-IN-1

Five theme-based titles in every collection

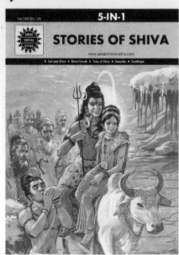

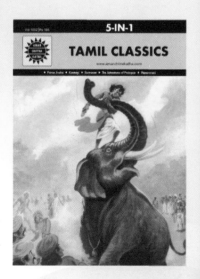

Hard-bound editions that every generation will cherish

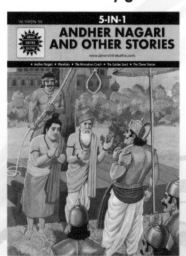

AMAR
CHITRA
KATHA

ULOOPI

THE NAGA PRINCESS WHO FELL IN LOVE WITH ARJUNA

The route to your roots

ULOOPI

Luck seemed to favour Arjuna. The Pandava was not only handsome and skilled but also a brave warrior. He won the hand of a beautiful princess but a past encounter with the mysterious Naga princess, Uloopi, remained with him like an enchanting dream. On that occasion, he had saved her life. Would she now work her charms to bring him back from the dead?

Script
Kamala Chandrakant

Illustrations
S.S.Havaldar

Editor
Anant Pai

Cover illustration by: V.B.Khalap

ULOOPI

ARJUNA, THE PANDAVA, ONCE BROKE A VOW. FOR THIS OFFENCE, HE HAD TO GO ON AN EXILE FOR TWELVE YEARS. ACCOMPANIED BY BRAHMANS HE SET OUT FROM INDRAPRASTHA, THE CAPITAL.

HIS FIRST HALT WAS AT GANGOTRI, THE SOURCE OF THE RIVER GANGA.

WHERE WILL WE GO FROM HERE?

I'LL VISIT THE HOLY PLACES OF THE LAND.

WHEREVER HE WENT, ARJUNA PERFORMED THE FIRE SACRIFICE. HE LOOKED UPON THIS AS HIS SACRED DUTY. SOMETIMES, A FIRE SACRIFICE CONTINUED FOR MANY DAYS.

ONE DAY, AS USUAL, ARJUNA WENT TO BATHE IN THE GANGA BEFORE BEGINNING THE SACRIFICIAL RITES.

AS HE WAS ABOUT TO STEP OUT—

I FEEL HELPLESS. I CAN'T MOVE A STEP FORWARD. AM I UNDER A SPELL?

THE BRAHMANS RUSHED FORWARD TO HIS RESCUE.

BUT WHEN THEY REACHED THE SPOT, ARJUNA HAD VANISHED FROM SIGHT.

ARJUNA WAS DRAGGED DEEP DOWN INTO THE RIVER TILL HE CAME TO A BEAUTIFUL PALACE.

I WONDER WHERE I AM, AND TO WHOM THIS PALACE BELONGS.

UNSEEN BY ARJUNA, A LADY WAS WATCHING HIM.

AH! A SACRIFICIAL FIRE! PERHAPS IT IS MEANT FOR ME.

HE SAT BEFORE THE SACRIFICIAL FIRE AND PERFORMED HIS RITES WITH DEVOTION.

AFTER FINISHING WHEN HE LIFTED HIS EYES—

I AM ULOOPI, THE DAUGHTER OF THE SNAKE-KING, KAURAVYA. YOU ARE IN THE UNDER-WATER CITY OF THE SNAKE-PEOPLE.

WHO ARE YOU?

WHY HAVE YOU BROUGHT ME HERE?

BECAUSE I LOVE YOU. PLEASE MAKE ME YOUR WIFE.

HOW CAN THAT BE POSSIBLE? I AM AN EXILED PRINCE.

IT IS THE DUTY OF A PRINCE TO RELIEVE THE DISTRESSED. IF YOU DO NOT AGREE TO MY PROPOSAL, I SHALL SURELY DIE.

MY FIRE SACRIFICE AT GANGOTRI IS INCOMPLETE.

I WILL TAKE YOU BACK TOMORROW. BUT PLEASE BE WITH ME TODAY.

ARJUNA WAS TOUCHED BY ULOOPI'S PLEADINGS.

I'LL DO WHAT YOU WISH, DEAR ONE!

THROUGHOUT THE HOURS OF HIS STAY, ULOOPI LOOKED AFTER HIS EVERY NEED WITH TENDERNESS AND AFFECTION.

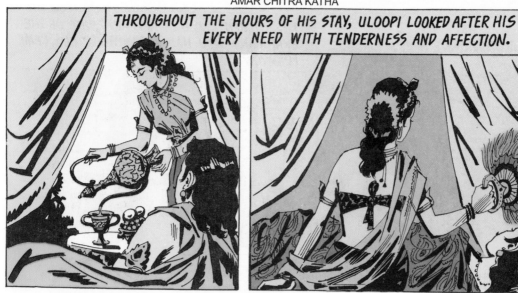

NEXT MORNING—

YOU HAVE SAVED MY LIFE. I AM GRATEFUL TO YOU, MY BELOVED HUSBAND. I SHALL TAKE YOU BACK, AS I PROMISED.

ULOOPI LED ARJUNA BACK TO THE SPOT FROM WHERE HER MAGICAL POWERS HAD DRAWN HIM.

HE WILL SOON FORGET ME.

AS ARJUNA EMERGED FROM THE WATER...

WHERE IS SHE? WHERE HAS SHE GONE?

...UNABLE TO BEAR THE GRIEF OF PARTING, ULOOPI HAD DISAPPEARED.

WHERE WERE YOU, O PANDAVA? WHAT HAPPENED?

THE MOMENT ARJUNA APPEARED, ONE OF THE BRAHMANS WHO HAD ACCOMPANIED HIM, CAME FORWARD.

AFTER TELLING THEM IN BRIEF WHAT BEFELL HIM, ARJUNA COMPLETED THE FIRE SACRIFICE.

THEN HE MADE A DECISION.

YOU MAY CONTINUE STAYING HERE IF YOU WISH. I INTEND VISITING THE HOLY PLACES IN THE EAST.

AND LEAVING THE BRAHMANS BEHIND, ARJUNA WENT EASTWARDS.

AFTER A LONG JOURNEY, HE REACHED MANIPUR.

AS HE WANDERED ON HE CAME UPON A PALACE.

HE ENTERED THE PALACE GARDENS...

... AND SUDDENLY STOPPED.

BEFORE HIM STOOD A VERY HANDSOME GIRL.

IS SHE ULOOPI?

HE WENT CLOSER STILL.

NO, SHE IS NOT ULOOPI.

WHO ARE YOU, FAIR MAIDEN?

I AM CHITRANGADA, THE DAUGHTER OF THE KING OF MANIPUR.

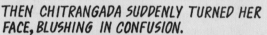

THEN CHITRANGADA SUDDENLY TURNED HER FACE, BLUSHING IN CONFUSION.

WHAT POWER IS IT THAT DRAWS ME TOWARDS HER?

I SHALL SEEK AN AUDIENCE WITH THE KING.

LATER, AT THE COURT—

O KING! I AM A NOBLE KSHATRIYA'S SON. I WISH TO MARRY YOUR DAUGHTER.

WHOSE SON ARE YOU, O VALIANT ONE?

I AM ARJUNA, THE SON OF PANDU.

ARJUNA! THE PANDAVA! YOU SHALL CERTAINLY MARRY MY DAUGHTER BUT...

...SHE IS MY ONLY CHILD. THE SON BORN TO HER MUST BECOME MY SUCCESSOR AND RULE MY KINGDOM AFTER ME.

IT SHALL BE AS YOU WISH, O KING.

IT IS THE GREAT PANDAVA, ARJUNA HOW FORTUNATE I AM!

ARJUNA MARRIED CHITRANGADA AND LIVED HAPPILY WITH HER AT MANIPUR.

MONTHS LATER A SON WAS BORN TO THEM.

HE SHALL BE CALLED BABHRUVAHANA.

GOOD. NOW IT IS TIME FOR ME TO CONTINUE ON MY PILGRIMAGE.

PLEASE STAY ON FOR SOME MORE TIME.

AS YOU WISH.

WHEN BABHRUVAHANA WAS OVER A YEAR OLD, ARJUNA LEFT MANIPUR.

MEANWHILE, ULOOPI HAD BEEN VERY UNHAPPY SINCE SHE PARTED FROM ARJUNA.

ARJUNA DOES NOT LOVE ME. THEREFORE I DON'T WANT TO GO TO HIM. BUT I CAN SPEND MY TIME WITH CHITRANGADA AND BABHRUVAHANA, WHOM HE LOVES.

ULOOPI DECIDED TO VISIT CHITRANGADA.

WHO ARE YOU, DEAR MAIDEN?

ULOOPI, THE DAUGHTER OF THE SNAKE-KING, KAURAVYA, YOUR CO-WIFE.

ULOOPI HAD CHANGED HER FORM BY HER MAGICAL POWERS.

I SUPPOSE, THIS IS OUR SON.

YES.

WHAT'S YOUR NAME?

BABHRUVAHANA.

HE SHALL BECOME A VALIANT PRINCE AND THE UNEQUALLED KING OF MANIPUR.

SOON—

I HAVE TO LEAVE NOW. BUT I SHALL OFTEN COME TO VISIT HIM.

WE SHALL AWAIT YOUR VISITS WITH PLEASURE, DEAR SISTER.

AS BABHRUVAHANA GREW UP, ULOOPI, TRUE TO HER WORD, OFTEN VISITED. SHE WIELDED A GREAT INFLUENCE OVER HIM.

IF YOU DO NOT PRACTISE YOUR ARCHERY, YOU WILL NEVER BECOME A GREAT HERO LIKE YOUR FATHER, ARJUNA.

YOU MUST LEARN TO CONCENTRATE. YOUR FATHER ACHIEVED MUCH BY HIS POWER OF CONCENTRATION.

ULOOPI TOLD HIM STORIES ABOUT ARJUNA'S ACHIEVEMENTS.

IS IT REALLY TRUE THAT HE HIT AT THE EYE OF THAT FISH BY LOOKING AT ITS IMAGE BELOW?

AND WHEN BABHRUVAHANA BECAME KING, AFTER HIS GRANDFATHER'S DEATH HE BECAME A FIT SUCCESSOR.

ULOOPI'S VISITS TO MANIPUR CONTINUED.

YOU HAVE MAGICAL POWERS, MOTHER! TELL ME, HOW IS MY FATHER?

YOUR FATHER AND UNCLES HAVE LOST THEIR KINGDOM TO THEIR COUSINS, THE KAURAVAS, IN A GAME OF DICE.

ONE DAY—

NOW YOUR FATHER IS PREPARING FOR THE BATTLE AGAINST THE KAURAVAS. IT IS TIME I LEFT.

MEANWHILE, AT THE BATTLE OF KURUKSHETRA, ARJUNA, SHIELDED BY SHIKHANDI, SHOWERED A VOLLEY OF ARROWS ON BHEESHMA, THE COMMANDER OF THE KAURAVAS.

BHEESHMA FELL, WOUNDED.

ALL THE CELESTIALS HAD GATHERED IN THE SKY TO WITNESS THIS BATTLE.

AMONG THEM WERE THE VASUS, THE BROTHERS OF BHEESHMA.

THAT WAS UNFAIR.

ARJUNA SHOULD BE PUNISHED.

THE VASUS WENT TO GANGA, THEIR MOTHER.

ARJUNA HAS SINNED. FOR THIS HE SHOULD GO TO HELL WHEN HE DIES.

SO BE IT.

ULOOPI, UNOBSERVED, HEARD EVERYTHING.

MY HUSBAND DOES NOT DESERVE SUCH A FATE. WORSE SINS HAVE BEEN COMMITTED ON THE BATTLEFIELD OF KURUKSHETRA.

SHE WENT TO HER FATHER, KAURAVYA.

FATHER, PLEASE SAVE MY HUSBAND FROM HELL.

DON'T WORRY, MY CHILD.

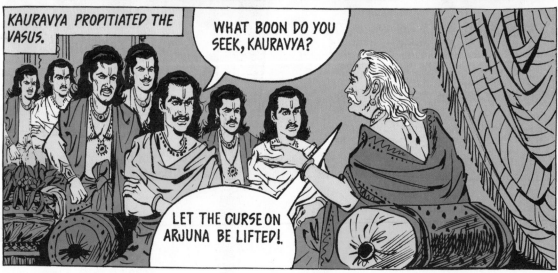

KAURAVYA PROPITIATED THE VASUS.

WHAT BOON DO YOU SEEK, KAURAVYA?

LET THE CURSE ON ARJUNA BE LIFTED!

THE CURSE WILL BE REDEEMED IF ARJUNA IS KILLED IN BATTLE BY HIS SON, BABHRUVAHANA.

KAURAVYA CAME BACK TO HIS DAUGHTER AND TOLD HER ABOUT IT.

THAT IS BAD. WHEN THE TIME COMES, I WILL HAVE TO BE THERE TO SAVE MY HUSBAND.

MEANWHILE, THE PANDAVAS HAD WON THE WAR AGAINST THE KAURAVAS...

... AND YUDHISHTHIRA, THE ELDEST OF THE PANDAVAS, WAS CROWNED KING.

SOON AFTERWARDS, YUDHISHTHIRA, DECIDED TO PERFORM THE HORSE SACRIFICE.

LET THE HORSE WANDER AT WILL OVER THE WHOLE EARTH, PROCLAIMING YOUR GLORY, O KING!

WHEN THE HORSE FOR THE SACRIFICE WAS SELECTED—

ARJUNA, YOU WILL PROTECT THE HORSE. YOU ALONE CAN DO IT.

AS THE HORSE WAS LET LOOSE AND ARJUNA PREPARED TO FOLLOW HIM—

THAT IS THE HORSE. IT WILL ROAM ABOUT IN DISTANT LANDS. IF ANY KING STOPS IT, HE WILL HAVE TO FIGHT WITH ARJUNA AND HIS ARMY.

AND IF A KING PERMITS THAT HORSE TO ROAM IN HIS KINGDOM, HE ACKNOWLEDGES YUDHISHTHIRA AS HIS SUPERIOR.

ARJUNA FOLLOWED THE SACRIFICIAL HORSE AS IT WANDERED AT WILL THROUGH VARIOUS KINGDOMS EITHER WINNING OR CONQUERING ALLIES FOR THE PANDAVAS.

AT LAST, THE HORSE ARRIVED AT THE KINGDOM OF MANIPUR.

A GREAT KINGDOM! MY SON IS ITS KING. I HOPE, HE PREPARES TO FIGHT WITH ME LIKE A TRUE KSHATRIYA.

BUT BABHRUVAHANA CAME FORWARD TO WELCOME HIM.

FATHER, I AM PROUD TO BE YOUR SON. I WELCOME YOU TO MY KINGDOM.

OH KING! THIS IS NOT PROPER. YOU HAVE FAILED IN YOUR DUTIES.

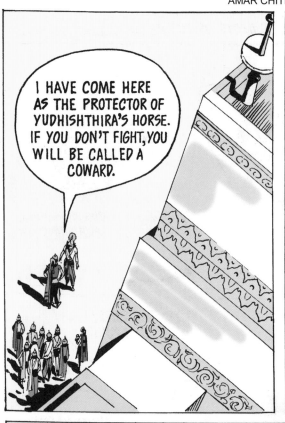

I HAVE COME HERE AS THE PROTECTOR OF YUDHISHTHIRA'S HORSE. IF YOU DON'T FIGHT, YOU WILL BE CALLED A COWARD.

BABHRUVAHANA WAS STUNNED BY THESE WORDS.

HOW CAN I FIGHT MY BELOVED FATHER?

JUST THEN, ULOOPI ARRIVED ON THE SCENE.

DO AS I TELL YOU, MY SON. DO NOT HESITATE. FIGHT YOUR FATHER. IT IS THE ONLY RIGHTEOUS AND DUTIFUL THING FOR YOU TO DO.

BABHRUVAHANA THOUGHT FOR A WHILE.

I HAVE LOST MY FATHER'S RESPECT. I CAN WIN IT BACK ONLY BY FIGHTING HIM. I WILL FIGHT.

HE PUT ON HIS ARMOUR, MOUNTED HIS CHARIOT, DROVE UP TO THE SACRIFICIAL HORSE...

...AND HAD IT SEIZED BY HIS MEN.

SEIZE THE HORSE OF HASTINAPURA!

AH! MY SON! MY SON! MY WORTHY SON!

ARJUNA CHECKED THE ADVANCE OF BABHRUVAHANA.

AN ARROW SENT BY BABHRUVAHANA PIERCED ARJUNA THROUGH THE SHOULDER.

WEAK WITH PAIN, ARJUNA RESTED AWHILE LEANING AGAINST HIS BOW, LOOKING ALMOST DEAD.

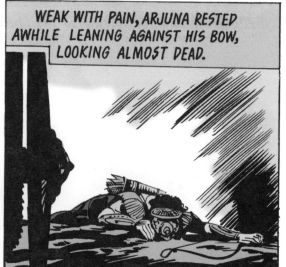

THEN AS HIS STRENGTH CAME BACK TO HIM

EXCELLENT! O SON OF CHITRANGADA! I AM PLEASED BY YOUR SKILL.

NOW FACE MY ARROWS AND FIGHT WITHOUT RUNNING AWAY.

BUT BABHRUVAHANA CUT ARJUNA'S ARROWS INTO BITS.

ARJUNA CUT OFF THE STANDARD ON BABHRUVAHANA'S CHARIOT AND...

...KILLED THE HORSES.

INFURIATED, BABHRUVAHANA GOT DOWN FROM HIS CHARIOT AND FOUGHT HIS FATHER ON FOOT.

ARJUNA ATTACKED HIM RELENTLESSLY TILL...

... BLINDED BY RAGE BABHRUVAHANA SHOT AN ARROW STRAIGHT INTO ARJUNA'S HEART.

ARJUNA DROPPED DEAD ON THE FIELD.

AT THE SAME MOMENT PARTLY THROUGH EXERTION BUT MORE OUT OF GRIEF BABHRUVAHANA FELL, UNCONSCIOUS.

AND ALL THE TIME ULOOPI STOOD WATCHING THE SCENE, UNPERTURBED, A PICTURE OF SERENITY.

A MESSENGER RAN TO CHITRANGADA.

I HAVE SAD NEWS FOR YOU. YOUR HUSBAND HAS BEEN KILLED BY THE KING WHO HIMSELF NOW LIES IN A SWOON.

CHITRANGADA TURNED PALE.

TAKE ME TO THE BATTLEFIELD.

AT THE BATTLEFIELD—

WHEN SHE CAME TO HER SENSES, SHE SAW ULOOPI.

O ULOOPI! I KNOW HOW DEVOTED YOU ARE TO OUR HUSBAND. YET I DO NOT FIND YOU GRIEVING.

WHEN ULOOPI SHOWED NO SIGN OF EMOTION, CHITRANGADA WENT TO ARJUNA.

RISE, DEAR HUSBAND. HERE IS THAT HORSE OF YOURS.

I HAVE SET IT FREE. YOU MUST FOLLOW IT AND PROTECT IT. RISE, DEAR HUSBAND, AND FULFIL YOUR DUTY.

SHE FOUND THAT ALL HER ATTEMPTS TO REVIVE ARJUNA WERE IN VAIN, SO SHE TURNED TO ULOOPI.

BRING HIM BACK TO LIFE, DEAR ULOOPI. I KNOW YOU CAN.

BUT ULOOPI REMAINED UNMOVED.

IF YOU DON'T, I SHALL GIVE UP MY LIFE.

CHITRANGADA SAT AT ARJUNA'S FEET.

JUST THEN BABHRUVAHANA REGAINED CONSCIOUSNESS.

ALAS! WHAT A PAINFUL SIGHT! MY MOTHER WHO HAS BEEN BROUGHT UP IN LUXURY, SITTING ON THE NAKED EARTH BESIDE MY DEAD FATHER. AND I KILLED HIM!

THEN HIS GAZE FELL ON ULOOPI.

O MOTHER! YOUR HEART SEEMS TO BE VERY HARD. IT DOES NOT BREAK EVEN ON SEEING YOUR HUSBAND LYING DEAD BEFORE YOU!

ULOOPI HEARD THESE ACCUSATIONS IN SILENCE.

WHY SHOULD IT? BY KILLING ARJUNA IN BATTLE I HAVE DONE WHAT YOU WANTED OF ME.

BUT FOR ME THERE IS NO REDEMPTION. I SHALL HAVE TO SINK INTO HELL. SO DREADFULLY HAVE I SINNED IN KILLING MY OWN FATHER.

BABHRUVAHANA WAS STRICKEN WITH GRIEF.

LISTEN MOTHER, IF MY FATHER DOES NOT COME BACK TO LIFE, I SHALL FOLLOW HIM.

I SHALL STARVE MYSELF TO DEATH RIGHT HERE ON THE BATTLEFIELD, NEXT TO MY FATHER. REJOICE MOTHER! YOUR SON TOO WILL DIE BEFORE YOUR EYES.

AND BABHRUVAHANA SAT NEXT TO HIS PARENTS.

ULOOPI WATCHED THE THREE OF THEM.

IT IS TIME I ACTED.

SHE CLOSED HER EYES AND THOUGHT OF THE GEM OF THE SNAKE PEOPLE, WHICH COULD REVIVE THE DEAD.

AND LO, THE GEM, THE MOST PRECIOUS POSSESSION OF THE SNAKE PEOPLE, CAME SAILING THROUGH THE SKIES...

... AND DROPPED INTO HER PALMS.

ULOOPI WENT TO BABHRUVAHANA.

RISE, O SON! YOUR FATHER HAS BEEN KILLED BY YOU FOR HIS OWN GOOD.

HE HAD BEEN CURSED BY THE VASUS TO GO TO HELL.

THE CURSE COULD BE REDEEMED ONLY IF YOU KILLED HIM IN THE BATTLEFIELD.

THE WORDS DID NOT CONSOLE BABHRUVAHANA.

THIS MAGIC GEM OF THE SNAKE PEOPLE CAN REVIVE THE DEAD. PLACE IT ON YOUR FATHER'S WOUND. HE WILL ARISE, AS VALIANT AS BEFORE.

BABHRUVAHANA WAS DELIGHTED.

DEAR MOTHER, HOW COULD I HAVE EVER DOUBTED YOU? PLEASE FORGIVE ME. I AM EVER GRATEFUL TO YOU.

HE WENT UP TO ARJUNA AND PLACED THE GEM ON HIS CHEST WHERE THE ARROW HAD PIERCED HIM.

ARJUNA WOKE UP RUBBING HIS EYES LIKE ONE WHO HAD BEEN FAST ASLEEP FOR A LONG TIME.

HE SAW BABHRUVAHANA LOOKING AT HIM IN WONDER.

MY SON, I AM PROUD OF YOU. YOUR VALOUR IS UNMATCHED!

ONLY THEN DID ARJUNA NOTICE CHITRANGADA AND ULOOPI. HE TURNED TO BABHRUVAHANA.

WHAT ARE YOUR MOTHERS DOING ON THE BATTLEFIELD?

BABHRUVAHANA BOWED HIS HEAD RESPECTFULLY.

MOTHER ULOOPI WILL EXPLAIN ALL.

ULOOPI TOLD ARJUNA ALL ABOUT THE CURSE OF THE VASUS.

BELOVED WIFE, I AM INDEBTED TO YOU. BOTH FOR THIS LIFE AND MY LIFE HERE-AFTER.

AND ULOOPI'S DREAM OF WINNING ARJUNA'S LOVE WAS FULFILLED.